THE VIRUS

Text © Miguel Chen
Illustration © David Buist

Editor: Amy Waeschle

ISBN: 978-1-7326982-8-4

Published by Zarfling Platoon
info@zarfling.com
zarfling.com

The parents were at work.
They were all happy too.

Everything was fine.

That night, the news came on to alert people about a virus.

To keep it from spreading,
everyone needed to be careful.

The virus could hurt a lot of people.

The parents became worried.

The kids got worried too.

Suddenly everything changed.

School was closed.

Work was closed.

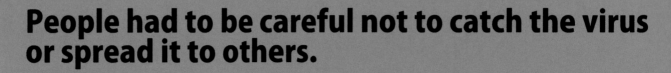

People had to be careful not to catch the virus or spread it to others.

Everyone stayed
home, to be safe.

People took care to cover their mouth if they coughed or sneezed.

Everyone washed their hands thoroughly and often.

They couldn't go to school or work, but the parents and kids were happy because they got to be together.

This extra time was special.

The parents and kids learned that they could be okay, even when things were uncertain.

They played and had fun together.

Everyone began appreciating each other on a deeper level.

After a while, the virus slowed down.

Health care workers and scientists worked together and got the virus under control.

People could go outside again.

The schools opened back up.

The parents could return to work.

Everyone played, and had fun, and remembered to wash their hands.

Everyone appreciated each other.
They all remembered what they'd learned.

We can be okay, even when things are uncertain, because we have each other.